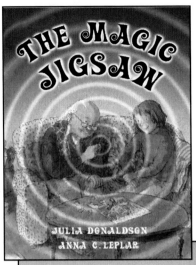

## The Magic Jigsaw

One moment, Jenny's making a jigsaw with Grandpa, the next she's travelling back in time. Can she escape the nasty housekeeper and make it back to the present?

## The fr[...]

Look at [...] front c[...]

Do you [...] Why?

## The back cover

The blurb on the back cover gives some clues about the story.

Do you think there is a link between the jigsaw and travelling in time?

## The title page

What does the picture show?

Why do you think there are two jigsaw pieces in the picture? Does this give you any clues about the story?

Are they from the same jigsaw puzzle?

What else is on this page? (*author, illustrator, publisher's logo*)

Julia Donaldson
Illustrated by Anna C. Leplar

1

# LESSON 1 (CHAPTER 1)

**READ**

## Read pages 2 to 5

***Purpose:*** To find out as much as possible about the character of Jane.

**EXPLORE**

## Pause at page 5

What do you learn about Jane from page 2?

Do you think the old house was the one where Grandpa's grandpa used to live? Why?

What did Jane do? Look at the illustration on page 5. What do you think is happening here?

**Tricky word (page 4):**
The word 'piece' may be beyond the children's word recognition skills. Tell this word to the children.

## Chapter 1

Grandpa loves jigsaw puzzles. We always do a jigsaw when I go to his house. Last week we did one of a horse.

"Isn't he a beauty, Jane?" said Grandpa.

I didn't say anything. I'm a bit scared of horses. I'm scared they might kick or bite.

The horse was standing outside an old house with tall windows. Grandpa said it looked like the house where *his* grandpa used to live.

We had almost finished the jigsaw.

"There's one piece missing," said Grandpa.

I found a piece under the table, but it was red, like Grandpa's carpet, and it was too big.

"It won't fit," I said. I put a finger into the gap in the jigsaw.

**READ**

# Read pages 6 to 9

***Purpose:*** To work out what has happened and be ready
to explain the story.

**EXPLORE**

# Pause at page 9

Has Jane seen the old house and the black horse
before? Where?

What do you think has happened?

How do you think Jane feels? Has she realised what
has happened?

Suddenly, the room started spinning around. I felt dizzy and closed my eyes. Then I felt thick hair under my finger.

When I opened my eyes, I saw an old house with tall windows. It looked just like the house in Grandpa's jigsaw.

What was happening?

My hands were holding something black, thick and hairy. It was a horse's mane, and I was sitting on the horse's back!

# Read pages 10 to 12

***Purpose:*** To look for clues as to where Jane is.

# Pause at page 12

Look at the illustrations on pages 10 and 11. What does the way the woman is dressed tell you?

Why does she think Jane is a boy? How would you feel if you were Jane?

Do you think Jane is inside Grandpa's jigsaw? Use information from the text to support your answer.

*Please turn to page 15 for Revisit and Respond activities.*

I looked down and saw a woman in a strange long dress. She looked angry.

"Get off that horse!" she said loudly. I slid quickly off the horse's back.

"You must be the new stable boy," she said. "Come with me."

Stable *boy*? Couldn't she see I was a girl? The woman took me to some stables. She pointed to a big white horse, and handed me a brush. I started to panic – what could I do? I was scared of the horse, but I was more scared of the woman.

"I'll be back soon," said the woman. Then she left.

I began to brush the horse. He didn't kick or bite, he just stood still. I didn't feel quite so scared any more, but I was still very confused. Where was I? Was I inside Grandpa's jigsaw?

# LESSON 2 (CHAPTER 2)

**RECAP**

## Recap lesson 1

What was Jane doing with Grandpa?

What unexpectedly happened?

Where has Jane ended up?

What has the scary woman made Jane do?

How do you think Jane will escape?

**READ**

## Read pages 13 to 15

***Purpose:*** To pick out all the unusual information about the house and the people.

**EXPLORE**

## Pause at page 15

Why does the woman get really angry?

What do you think about the house Jane is in? Is it like your house? What are the differences?

Who do you think is in the bed? What will happen next?

**Tricky word (page 13):**
The word 'old-fashioned' may be beyond the children's word recognition skills. Tell this word to the children.

**Tricky word (page 15):**
The word 'phew' may also want to be discussed as a tricky word.

### Chapter 2

After a while, the woman came back. She took
me into a big kitchen with an old-fashioned
stove. She pushed some bread and cheese
into my hands.

There was a knock on the door. The woman
opened it. A boy stood there.

"I'm the new stable boy," he said.

The woman looked at the boy, and then she
looked at me. She looked angry again –
*really* angry.

I ran out of the room and up some
stairs. I could hear the woman's footsteps
behind me. I ran along a hallway, opened
a door, and slipped in.

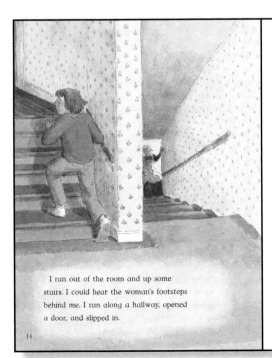

I stood still, and I heard the woman's
footsteps go past the room. Phew! I had
escaped her!

I looked around the room. There was a big
bed with a curtain around it. Suddenly,
a voice said, "Hello!" and a hand pulled
the curtain back.

14

15

9

**READ**

# Read pages 16 to 19

***Purpose:*** To think about who the boy might be.

**EXPLORE**

# Pause at page 19

The boy thinks Jane looks strange.

Why does Jane think the boy looks strange?

Who do you think the boy is? Why?

How do you think the jigsaw could help Jane?

A boy was sitting up in bed. He wore a nightshirt and had red spots all over his face.

"You'd better go away," he said. "You might catch chicken pox."

"I've had chicken pox. I won't catch it," I said.

"Oh good," said the boy. "I'm so bored. I've almost finished this jigsaw."

The jigsaw was of a room.

"That looks just like my grandpa's living room," I said.

"It's a strange room," said the boy. "And you look quite strange too."

I thought *he* was the one who looked strange, but I didn't say so.

I helped the boy finish the jigsaw, but the last piece didn't fit.

**READ**

# Read pages 20 to 23

***Purpose:*** To find out what happened to Jane.

**EXPLORE**

# Pause at page 23

What makes you think the jigsaw could be magic?

Why does Jane stop the boy putting in the final piece of the jigsaw? (*So she can transport herself forward in time.*)

Where do you think Jane will end up?

"I need a big red piece," said the boy,
"but there's only a little black piece left."
He handed it to me.

I took the big red piece that didn't fit
Grandpa's jigsaw out of my pocket.

"Try this one," I said.

Suddenly, I heard footsteps again. The
door handle turned. It was the woman
coming back!

"Wait!" I said. "Don't put that piece in yet."

I put my finger into the gap in the jigsaw.
Yes! I could feel carpet! The boy's room
started spinning round, and I closed my eyes.

When I opened my eyes, I was back in Grandpa's living room! The horse jigsaw was still there, with one piece missing. I reached into my pocket and took out the little black piece. I pushed it into the gap.

"Yes! It fits!" I said.

**READ**

# Read to the end

*Purpose:* To find out if Jane goes back to Grandpa's living room.

**EXPLORE**

# Pause at page 24

How did Jane manage to get back?

Did she enjoy her adventure?

What would have happened if she couldn't find the piece?

# After Reading
## Revisit and Respond
## Lesson 1

- What do you know about the character of Jane? Write a character profile of Jane using information gleaned from the story so far.

- What clues can you find in the text and pictures to suggest that Jane has gone back in time?

## Lesson 2

- Why is the woman angry on page 13? What does she think has happened? How does the author create a sense of mystery? (*strangeness of things*) How does the author create tension? (*the role of the woman*)

- Role-play the story. Have one person take the role of Jane and (hot seating) answer questions about the adventure.

- Compare this story to *Tiger Hunt* (Rigby Star Gold Level). How do the stories create a sense of strange happenings?

- Discuss the settings of the story, and how time-travel is used to change the setting. Ask the children to brainstorm other time-travel settings, e.g. *land of dinosaurs, Roman times*.

# Follow-up

## Independent Group Activity Work

This book is accompanied by two photocopy masters, one with a reading focus, and one with a writing focus, which support the teaching objectives of this book. The photocopy masters can be found in the Planning and Assessment Guide.

**PCM F3.1** (*reading*)

**PCM F3.2** (*writing*)

You may also like to invite the children to read the text again during their independent reading (either at school or at home).

## Writing

**Guided writing:** Brainstorm and then plan (using a flow chart) how to write an alternative ending to the story.

**Extended writing:** Write a different ending – possibly one where Jane had to find a different way back.

# Assessment Points

*Assess that the children have learnt the main teaching points of the book by checking that they can:*

- draw together ideas and information from across a whole text, using simple signposts in the text (e.g. using both text and picture clues when finding information).